# Molly and the Giant

Story by Julia Jarman
Pictures by Sholto Walker

OXFORD
UNIVERSITY PRESS

Long, long ago, when there were still wolves in the woods, there lived a girl called Molly Whipple. She had a mother and a father and two older sisters, Polly and Dolly, and she was small for her age. Polly and Dolly sometimes laughed at Molly, because she was so little, but one day when the three sisters got lost in the woods, Molly proved she was as brave as a bear.

Look!

Dolly cried, "We're lost! We're lost!"
Polly cried, "We'll never find our way
home!"

But Molly said, "Of course we will, if
we keep our wits about us. Look, there's
a house. Let's ask for help."

3

The house was as big as a castle. Who lived there?

When Molly knocked on the door an old woman peered out.

"Can I help you?" she asked.

"I hope so," said Molly. "We are lost. Please would you help us find our way home?"

"Of course," said the old woman. "Come in and sit down. When my husband gets back from market he will take you home."

"He loves children," she added, as she closed the door – and Molly noticed an enormous plate on the table, and an enormous pot on the stove.

Uh-oh!

"Polly, Dolly...," Molly took their hands. "I think it would be better to make our own way home."

But before they could reach the door it crashed open, and ...

... in stomped a terrible giant!

The giant seized Polly and Dolly,
and put them on his plate.
"I will eat these two now. Raw!"
he roared. "Get me a drink, wife!"

6

"Fee fi fo fum!
Three little girls,
Yum, yum, yum!"

Polly and Dolly froze with fear as the giant lifted them to his mouth.

But, quick as a cat, Molly jumped onto the table.

"Mr Giant," she asked politely, "don't you think my sisters are very thin?"

"Yes," said the giant grumpily.

"Wouldn't fat children be tastier?" said Molly.

"Yes," said the giant. "Fat children would be delicious."

"Well," said Molly. "There are three fat children hiding upstairs."

"Fat children? Upstairs!"
The giant sprang to his feet.

"Three fat children!
Yum, yum, yum!
More delicious food
for my tum, tum, tum!"

Dropping Polly and Dolly, he rushed to the
stairs and – one, two, three – Molly, Polly and
Dolly jumped out of the window!

And back came the giant.
"I couldn't see the fat children,"
he grumbled.
Then he saw the empty room and –
through the open window – the girls
running through the woods.

9

With a roar he set off after them.

The girls ran fast, but the giant ran faster. He took enormous strides. Closer and closer he got.

"Quick! Quick!" Molly urged her sisters, as the ground shook. "There's a bridge ahead. It's called One Hair Bridge! Cross it and we'll be safe!"

Closer and closer the giant got.

They could feel his breath hot as fire, but, fast as ferrets, they ran and ran till they reached the bridge – and crossed it!

Then they laughed at the giant, who couldn't cross the narrow bridge, because he was much too wide. All he could do was pull his hair and stamp his feet and roar.

"If ever again you cross my path,
You will feel a giant's wrath.
I will beat you,
I will eat you
If you come this way again!"

13

Molly and her sisters ran on till they came to a palace.

Molly demanded to see the King.

"Do you know you've got a terrible giant in your land who eats children?" she asked.

"Y-yes," stammered the King.

"So why don't you get rid of him?"

"B-because he's b-bigger than me and he's got a m-magic sword," said the King.

"Well, you should get rid of it," said Molly.

14

Now the King could see that Molly was brave and clever.

"Couldn't **you** get the magic sword, Molly?" he suggested.

"What would you give me if I did?" said Molly.

"Your sister Polly could marry my son, Prince Roland," said the King.

Now Polly had fallen in love with Roland, and Roland had fallen in love with Polly.

So Molly said, "Yes, Your Majesty. I will get the giant's magic sword."

15

That night Molly
went back to the giant's
house.

She saw the giant sleeping,
his magic sword by his side.

She crept in and took hold of
his sword – and the giant woke up!

Molly ran.

"Stop!" roared the giant, jumping out
of bed.

But Molly kept running, dragging the
sword behind her.

And the giant got closer. He took
enormous strides, but Molly reached One
Hair Bridge first. She ran over it, and all
the giant could do was pull his hair,
stamp his feet, and roar.

"If ever again you cross my path,
You will feel a giant's wrath.
I will beat you,
I will eat you
If you come this way again!"

Molly went back to the King and gave him the magic sword. He was pleased but he soon wanted something more.

"The giant has a magic purse," he said. "Could you get that for me, Molly?"

"What would you give me if I did?" she asked.

"Your sister, Dolly, could marry my son Prince Walter," said the King.

Now Dolly had fallen in love with Walter, and Walter had fallen in love with Dolly.

So Molly said, "All right, Your Majesty. I will get the magic purse."

That night she went back to the giant's house.

She saw the giant sleeping with his magic purse under his pillow.

She crept in, pulled it out – and the giant woke up.

Molly ran.
The giant ran with enormous strides.
But Molly reached One Hair Bridge first and ran over it.
Once again, all the giant could do was pull his hair and stamp his feet and roar angrily.

"If ever again you cross my path,
You will feel a giant's wrath.
I will beat you,
I will eat you
If you come this way again!"

Molly took the purse to the King. He was pleased, but, again, he wanted something more – the giant's magic ring.

"But that's on his finger!" said Molly. "What would you give me if I got it?"

"Prince Timothy, my youngest son," said the King. Now Molly liked Timothy and Timothy liked Molly very much, but Molly didn't want to get married – well, not yet.

So she said, "No thank you, Your Majesty, but I would like a palace of my own, please."

The King said, "Yes Molly. Of course, Molly. Anything you say, Molly."

21

That night Molly went back to the giant's house. She looked through the window and saw the magic ring shining on his finger.

In she crept and gently pulled at it, but the ring wouldn't come off. She pulled again – and the giant stirred.

Molly dived under the bed and waited till the giant went back to sleep.

Then silently, she crept to the kitchen, got two useful things, and went back to the giant.

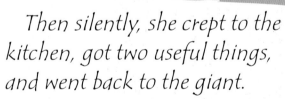

First she smeared his finger with butter.

Then she pulled

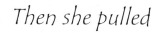

and off came the ring – as the giant grabbed her!

Well he thought it was her. "Got you, Molly! Got you!" He laughed and laughed – and Molly laughed silently, hiding under the bed.

"Now I'll eat you, head first!" roared the giant. He took a big bite – of the ladle! For clever Molly had tricked him.

"Ouch!" She heard him roar. Crunch! Clatter! Crash! His teeth fell to the floor like boulders down a cliff.

23

Quick as a cat, Molly raced back to the palace, where she gave the ring to the King.

"Thank you, Molly. There's your palace," said the King.

"And there are Mother and Father!" cried Molly, running to meet Mr and Mrs Whipple, who had been looking for their daughters for three whole days. "They can live in the palace with me!"

So Molly and her family, the King and his family, and all the people in the land lived happily ever after.

As for the giant, without his magic he started to shrink, and one day he vanished completely!